Killer Plants

by Helen Orme

Ransom

Trailblazers

Killer Plants
by Helen Orme
Educational consultant: Helen Bird

Illustrated by Jan Martin

Published by Ransom Publishing Ltd.
51 Southgate Street, Winchester, Hants. SO23 9EH
www.ransom.co.uk

ISBN   978 184167 803 0

First published in 2009

Killer Plants

Contents

Killer Plants

Get the facts

How can plants be killers?

Some plants are **poisonous**. They may kill people, or animals, who eat them.

Some plants kill other plants by taking over their **habitats** (the places where they live).

Some plants even kill other creatures for food.

How?

All plants make **food** from **sunlight**, but they need other things as well. They usually get these from the soil.

In places where the soil is poor, some plants have found other ways to get the extra things they need.

They have turned into meat-eaters!

What meat do they eat?

Most **carnivorous** (meat-eating) plants eat **insects** – but some may eat bigger creatures!

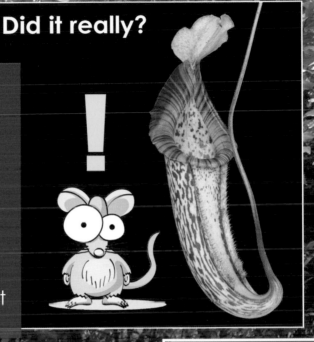

Did it really?

In 2006 a plant growing in a **Botanical Garden** in France ate a **mouse**!

The body of the mouse was found inside the plant, after visitors **complained** about the smell.

The tree of death

The **bunya-bunya tree** is known as the **tree of death**. The cones of this tree weigh up to 7 kilos. If you are walking under one of these trees and a cone falls on your head, you'll probably end up dead.

(If you survive, you can eat the nuts in the cone – they taste great!)

Carnivorous plants

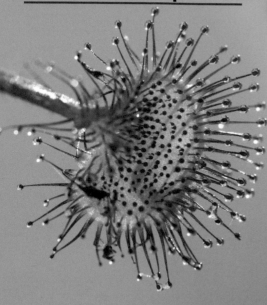

How do plants catch other creatures?

The **sundew** has **sticky hairs** on its leaves. Once an insect lands on the plant, it can't escape.

These hairs make **digestive juice**, as well as the sticky stuff, and the prey is soon eaten.

When an insect lands on the leaves of the **Venus fly trap**, its leaves close over the insect and trap it.

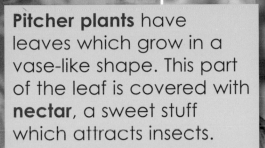

Pitcher plants have leaves which grow in a vase-like shape. This part of the leaf is covered with **nectar**, a sweet stuff which attracts insects.

As the **insects** go into the plant, they get trapped. They fall to the bottom, where there is a pool of juice to digest them.

The biggest pitcher plants can grow up to 30 cm long and have eaten **frogs** and **rats**!

The fastest killers, **bladderworts**, use a sort of trap-door to get their prey. They can suck in an insect in a 50th of a second!

Deadly poisons

Do you know a plant that contains the deadly poison **cyanide**?

DANGER

Here's one – an apple!

The **poison** is in the **pips** – but you would have to eat hundreds of them to get ill.

And if you don't chew them, they will pass straight through you.

Some plants have parts that are good to eat, but have **leaves**, **roots** or **seeds** which are **poisonous**.

Rhubarb is good to eat raw or cooked, but the leaves are poisonous! Luckily, you would have to eat quite a lot of them – and they don't taste good!

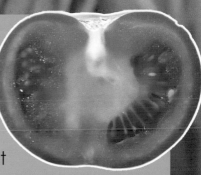

Potatoes and **tomatoes** belong to the same plant family. Both have parts that are poisonous enough to make you ill.

Don't eat their leaves or shoots. (Or the potato fruits that look just like baby tomatoes!)

So what is the world's most dangerous plant?

These **castor bean** seeds look harmless, but they can kill.

They contain a poison called **ricin**.

This is **12,000 times** more toxic than rattlesnake venom!

In 1978 a man was **murdered** in **London**. A pellet of **ricin** was shot into his leg from a gun disguised as an umbrella.

Deadly fungi

Death cap

It's easy to pick poisonous mushrooms by mistake. So if you feel like going hunting for wild fungi to eat – **DON'T!**

The biggest killer of humans is the death cap.

If you eat this you will feel dizzy and find it hard to breathe. Then you start to be very sick. After about three days you think you are getting better.

Are you? Sorry, no! Your liver is being destroyed. After about six days you will probably die!

Ergot

Ergot is a tiny fungus which grows on wheat. Sometimes people eat the fungus with the wheat. It causes burning feelings in the arms and legs. Then people start to see things that aren't there. It can be a killer.

At the end of the 17th century, in America, people in the town of _____ thought that there were _____ living there.

It started when some people began to have fits. They screamed, threw things, and said they were being pricked by pins.

They were accused of being witches. _____ of people were _____ .

Some people think that the whole town had eaten flour with _____ in it, and that this caused the problem.

What is the biggest living thing in the world?

A whale? A tree? No! It's a fungus!

The biggest honey fungus in the world is in Oregon, USA. It is over two thousand years old, covers an area of nearly nine square kilometres – and it's a killer.

It doesn't kill people, though. It kills other plants. And when they're dead, it feeds on their rotting remains ...

Honey fungus

Invasion of the killer aliens

Plants that escape into new **habitats** are called **aliens** – and they can be deadly!

People with gardens like to grow plants that are **new** and **different**. They like plants that come from **distant countries**.

Sometimes, this is a really bad idea!

Gardeners in Europe thought **floating pennywort** from North America was just the thing for their ponds.

But it escaped into the wild, and grew like a **thick mat** over the water, using up **oxygen** needed by fish and other creatures.

One of the worst invaders is **Japanese knotweed**.

It can grow through walls, paths and roads, and causes a lot of problems. It is very hard to get rid of it as it will grow from very tiny pieces.

In many countries it is **against the law** to plant it. But the Japanese knotweed just keeps on growing ...

Watch out – there's a giant lurking down by the river that can injure you. **Giant hogweed** is huge – and it's crowding out native plants.

It has a great way of defending itself – if you touch the plant, it has **chemicals** that can **burn** you. Spreading this plant is against the law.

Frankencrops

People have always tried to change the plants they grow. They want flowers to smell better, or to have lots of different colours.

They want to make food crops which will **taste better** or will feed more people. They want to grow food crops that **insects** won't want to eat.

In the past it took a long time to develop new plants, but now **scientists** can make big changes very quickly by changing the **genes** in the plants.

Many people think that it is bad to change plants like this. They call food made from GM (**Genetically Modified**) crops '**Frankenfood**'.

GM crops are bad!

(Frankenstein's monster is a character from a story. In the story, the monster is made from odd bits of other people's bodies. The monster isn't friendly and kills people.)

Protest over GM crops

Arguments for GM plants

- ✓ There is no proof that GM foods are unsafe.

- ✓ GM plants can be made to grow with less water.

- ✓ They can be made to resist pests and plant viruses.

- ✓ They will help to feed people in developing countries.

What do you think?

Arguments against GM plants

- ✗ GM plants might affect existing food crops if their pollen spreads.

- ✗ GM crops might harm wild animals, birds and insects.

No they aren't!

Chapter 1:
Look at this!

Mr Potts loved growing things. He grew flowers. He grew vegetables. He grew shrubs and trees.

But, best of all, he liked growing things from seed. Not just seeds from packets. That was too easy. What he really liked was growing the seeds from things he had eaten. If it had a seed, he planted it.

One day, in the greenhouse, he found a strange seed. He showed it to his next door neighbour, Mrs Dyer.

'Look at this,' he said. 'I've never seen anything like it.'

Mr Potts found a strange seed in his greenhouse.
He showed it to his neighbour.

'What are you going to do with it?' asked Mrs Dyer.

'Plant it, of course,' he said.

The seed grew quickly. Mr Potts talked to it every day. He thought talking to plants made them grow better.

'You are a pretty little thing,' he told the shoot. 'What lovely leaves you've got.'

It grew really well.

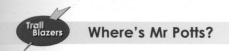
Chapter 2:
The flower

'Look!' he said to Mrs Dyer. 'It's got a bud.'

The plant grew taller.

'I shall have to feed it,' he told Mrs Dyer.

'Whatever do you feed a plant on?' asked Mrs Dyer. 'It hasn't got a mouth.'

Mr Potts laughed.

'This,' he said. 'It's plant food. I put it in the water.'

The plant grew and grew.

Mr Potts took it out of its pot and planted it in the soil. The flower opened. It was huge.

'What is it?' asked Mrs Dyer.

'It's called a pitcher plant,' said Mr Potts. 'But I didn't know they could get so big.'

They watched the plant. A bee landed on the edge of the flower. It buzzed loudly and tried to fly off. It slipped into the trumpet. It buzzed even louder.

Then it stopped.

Chapter 3:
The heap of bones

'It's eaten the bee,' said Mr Potts.

'Ugh!' said Mrs Dyer.

'What's that smell?' asked Mrs Dyer.

'That's how it attracts insects,' said Mr Potts.

'It's very bad,' said Mrs Dyer. 'It smells like rotten meat.'

Later that night, Mr Potts went to say goodnight to his plant.

Under the flower was a heap of bones.

'It's eaten a mouse,' thought Mr Potts. 'That's what the smell was.'

Mrs Dyer brought some meat scraps round.

'Do you think it would like these?' she asked.

'You look upset,' said Mr Potts. 'Is everything alright?'

'Have you seen my cat around?' asked Mrs Dyer. 'He hasn't been home for two days and I'm a bit worried.'

'Oh dear,' said Mr Potts. 'I'll keep a look out.'

Mr Potts went to say goodnight to his plant.

Under the flower was a heap of bones.

Chapter 4:
What can I give it tomorrow?

Mr Potts looked at the bones. 'They look like cat bones.' he thought.

He looked at the plant. 'You're growing too fast,' he said. 'You mustn't eat cats!'

'I know!' he told it. 'I'll find you a nice steak.'

Mr Potts was worried. The plant was still growing. And it was hungry.

'It's costing me a fortune,' he thought. 'Whatever can I feed it next?'

'Mr Potts,' called Mrs Dyer. 'Where are you?'

There was no one in the house. Mrs Dyer went to the greenhouse.

The plant was even bigger. It reached right up to the roof.

Under the flower was a heap of bones. Mrs Dyer bent over to look at them.

And, as she bent over, so did the flower ...

After a while Mr Potts came out of his shed.

Under the flower was a pair of boots.

'Now,' thought Mr Potts. 'What can I give it tomorrow?'

Killer Plants word check

aliens	habitat
carnivorous	invaders
cyanide	nectar
developing countries	oxygen
digestive	poisonous
fungi	pollen
genes	prey
GM (Genetically Modified)	survive
	venom
	virus